ARCADE WORLD

ZOMBIE INVADERS

ARCADE WORLD

ZOMBIE INVADERS

WRITTEN BY **NATE BITT**
ILLUSTRATED BY **JOÃO ZOD**
AT GLASS HOUSE GRAPHICS

SCHOLASTIC INC.

ISBN 978-1-339-00589-8

12 11 10 9 8 7 6 5 4 3 2 1   23 24 25 26 27 28

PRINTED IN THE U.S.A.   40

FIRST SCHOLASTIC PRINTING, JANUARY 2023

TEXT BY MATTHEW J. GILBERT
DESIGNED BY NICK SCIACCA
ART SERVICES BY GLASS HOUSE GRAPHICS
ART BY: JOÃO ZOD, MARCELO SALAZA & WATS
COLORS BY: MARCOS PELANDRA & KAMUI
LETTERING BY: MARCOS INOUE
THE ILLUSTRATIONS FOR THIS BOOK WERE RENDERED DIGITALLY.
THE TEXT OF THIS BOOK WAS SET IN CC SAMARITAN.

CONTENTS

CHAPTER 1

WHERE TO BEGIN?

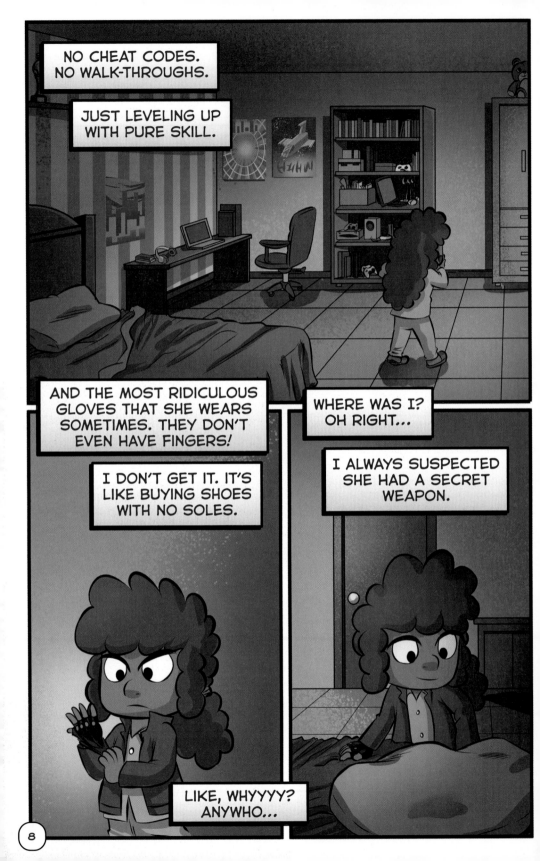

NO CHEAT CODES.
NO WALK-THROUGHS.

JUST LEVELING UP
WITH PURE SKILL.

AND THE MOST RIDICULOUS
GLOVES THAT SHE WEARS
SOMETIMES. THEY DON'T
EVEN HAVE FINGERS!

I DON'T GET IT. IT'S
LIKE BUYING SHOES
WITH NO SOLES.

WHERE WAS I?
OH RIGHT...

I ALWAYS SUSPECTED
SHE HAD A SECRET
WEAPON.

LIKE, WHYYYY?
ANYWHO...

HOW ELSE WOULD SHE KNOW *EVERY SINGLE* TRICK IN THE BOOK?

HELLO MY NAME IS...

Totally not a secret diary so stay out!

TIME FOR MY MORNING WORKOUT.

I SUPPOSE, TO BE THE BEST, YOU HAVE TO BE PREPARED TO FACE ANY CHALLENGE.

...CREEEEEAK

GUUUUUHHHHH...

NO MATTER HOW SCARY.

YOU HAVE TO PLAY WITHOUT FEAR.

HEY, WAIT A SEC—

I THOUGHT YOU WEREN'T COMING TO ARCADE WORLD!

IS *THIS* THE FAMOUS ARCADE WORLD?! I THOUGHT IT WAS THE PETTING ZOO.

YOU'RE WEIRD, TRAVIS.

YEAH, I KNOW. THIS PLACE PUTS ME IN A MOOD.

CHAPTER 2

NEWS FLASH: *BEAT* THEM?!

NEWS FLASH: JOURNEY, I STILL WEAR A T-SHIRT WHEN I GO SWIMMING.

SO?

SO? SO!

SO, *NEWS FLASH:* I'M NOT A RISK-TAKER-TYPE GUY.

AND ANOTHER NEWS FLASH—

UGH, WOULD YOU STOP SAYING—

NEWS FLASH!

NEWS FLAAAAASH!

PARKING LOT

NEWS FLASH: THINGS WERE ABOUT TO GET EVEN WEIRDER.

THE DEAD HAVE RISEN! AND THEY'RE INVADING THE MALL!

EXTRA! EXTRA! READ ALL ABOUT IT IN TODAY'S ZOMBIE **DEAD**LINE NEWS!

23

PLAYER ONE PLAYER TWO

PLAYER ONE

WHATEVER YOU DO, DON'T OPEN THAT PAPER—

ZOMBIES INVADE NORMAL M

Run, don't walk, to the newly redecorated Nor-Mall for a one-of-a-kind shopping experience! And remember to visit the food court so we—oh whoops, we mean, YOU—have a bite to eat! It's completely safe! Bring the whole family down.

aaahhh!! aaahhh!! aaahhh!! aaahhh!!
aaahhh!! aaahhh!! uaaaaa.... aaahhh!!
aaahhh!! uaaaaa... uaaaaa... uaaaaa...
brainssss... aaaahhhhh... uaaaaa.....aahh
aaaahhhhh... uaaaaaa... brainssss... aahh
uaaaaa....brainsss...aaahhhhh uaaaa.....aah
aaaahhhhh...uaaaaaaa...brainssss... aaahh!!!
aaahhh!! aaahhh!! aaahhh!! aaahhh!!
aaahhh!! aaahhh!! uaaaaa.... aaahhh!!
aahh!! uaaaaa... uaaaaa... uaaaaa...
rinssss... aaaahhhhh... uaaaaa.....aahh
hhhhh... uaaaaaa... brainssss... aahh
aa....brainsss...aaahhhhh uaaaa.....aah
hhh...uaaaaaaa...brainssss... aaahh!!!

aaahhh!! aaahhh!! aaahhh!! aaahhh!!
aaahhh!! aaahhh!! uaaaaa.... aaahhh!!
aaahhh!! uaaaaa... uaaaaa... uaaaaa...
brainsss... aaaahhhhh... uaaaaa.....
aaaahhhhh... uaaaaaa... brainssss... aahh
uaaaaa....brainsss...aaahhhhh uaaaa.....aah
aaaahhhhh...uaaaaaaa...brainssss... aaahh!!!
aaahhh!! aaahhh!! aaahhh!! aaahhh!!
aaahhh!! uaaaaa... uaaaaa... aaahhh!!
brainssss... aaaahhhhh... uaaaaa...
aaaahhhhh... uaaaaaa... brainssss.....aahh
uaaaaa....brainsss...aaahhhhh uaaaa.....aah
aaaahhhhh...uaaaaaaa...brainssss... aaahh!!!

Zombie Chef Zombino's promise: *"Only serve the flesh-est ingredients!"*

a
aa
aaa
brai
aaaa
uaaaa

Miss Zombie!!

aaahhh!! aaahhh!! aaahhh!! aaahhh!!
aaahhh!! aaahhh!! uaaaaa.... aaahhh!!
aaahhh!! uaaaaa... uaaaaa... uaaaaa...
brainssss... aaaahhhhh... uaaaaa.....aahh
aaaahhhhh... uaaaaaa... brainssss... aahh
uaaaaa....brainsss...aaahhhhh uaaaa....aah
aaaahhhh...uaaaaaaa...brainssss... aaahh!!!
aaahhh!! aaahhh!! aaahhh!! aaahhh!!
aaahhh!! aaahhh!! uaaaaa.... aaahhh!!
aaahhh!! uaaaaa... uaaaaa... uaaaaa...
brainssss... aaaahhhhh... uaaaaa.....aahh
aaaahhhhh... uaaaaaa... brainssss... aahh
uaaaaa....brainsss...aaahhhhh uaaaa....aah
aaaahhhh...uaaaaaaa...brainssss... aaahh!!!

aaahhh!! aaahhh!! aaahhh!! aaahhh!!
aaahhh!! aaahhh!! uaaaaa.... aaahhh!!
aaahhh!! uaaaaa... uaaaaa... uaaaaa...
brainssss... aaaahhhhh... uaaaaa.....aahh
aaaahhhhh... uaaaaaa... brainssss... aahh
uaaaaa....brainsss...aaahhhhh uaaaa....aah
aaaahhhh...uaaaaaaa...brainssss... aaahh!!!

aaahhh!! aaahhh!! aaahhh!! aaahhh!!
aaahhh!! aaahhh!! uaaaaa.... aaahhh!!
aaahhh!! uaaaaa... uaaaaa... uaaaaa...
brainssss... aaaahhhhh... uaaaaa.....aahh
aaaahhhhh... uaaaaaa... brainssss... aahh
uaaaaa....brainsss...aaahhhhh uaaaa....aah
aaaahhhh...uaaaaaaa...brainssss... aaahh!!!

aaahhh!! aaahhh!! aaahhh!! aaahhh!!
aaahhh!! aaahhh!! uaaaaa.... aaahhh!!
aaahhh!! uaaaaa... uaaaaa... uaaaaa...
brainssss... aaaahhhhh... uaaaaa.....aahh
aaaahhhhh... uaaaaaa... brainssss... aahh
uaaaaa....brainsss...aaahhhhh uaaaa....aah
aaaahhhh...uaaaaaaa...brainssss... aaahh!!!

The Best Zombie Barbershop!

aaahhh!! aaahhh!! aaahhh!! aaahhh!!
aaahhh!! aaahhh!! uaaaaa.... aaahhh!!
aaahhh!! uaaaaa... uaaaaa... uaaaaa...
brainssss... aaaahhhhh... uaaaaa.....aahh
aaaahhhhh... uaaaaaa... brainssss... aahh
uaaaaa....brainsss...aaahhhhh uaaaa....aah
aaaahhhh...uaaaaaaa...brainssss... aaahh!!!
aaahhh!! aaahhh!! aaahhh!! aaahhh!!
aaahhh!! aaahhh!! uaaaaa.... aaahhh!!
aaahhh!! uaaaaa... uaaaaa... uaaaaa...
brainssss... aaaahhhhh... uaaaaa.....aahh
aaaahhhhh... uaaaaaa... brainssss... aahh
uaaaaa....brainsss...aaahhhhh uaaaa....aah
aaaahhhh...uaaaaaaa...brainssss... aaahh!!!

hh!! aaahhh!! aaahhh!! aaahhh!!
h!! aaahhh!! uaaaaa.... aaahhh!!
a!! uaaaaa... uaaaaa... uaaaaa...
ss... aaaahhhhh... uaaaaa.....aahh
hh... uaaaaaa... brainssss... aahh
brainsss...aaahhhhh uaaaa....aah
..uaaaaaaa...brainssss... aaahh!!!
aahhh!! aaahhh!! aaahhh!!
aahhh!! uaaaaa.... aaahhh!!
aaaa... uaaaaa... uaaaaa...
aaahhhhh... uaaaaa.....aahh
uaaaaaa... brainssss... aahh
sss...aaahhhhh uaaaa....aah

AND WITH THAT LITTLE PEP TALK OUT OF THE WAY, WE WERE OFF TO FACE THE ZOMBIE HORDE.

NORMAL MALL

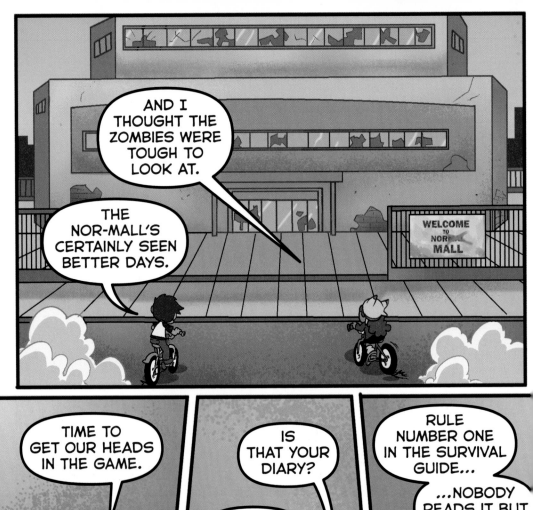

34

SHE *DIDN'T.*

BUT SHE WENT IN ANYWAY.

AND SO DID I.

PYOOOOOM!

SMASH! -SM -SMAAASH!

-SM

-SMASH!

VRRRRR!

IS THAT A DRONE?

WHOA! GUESS WE'RE LEVELING UP.

AND I DIDN'T EVEN GET A MALL PRETZEL.

WHO NEEDS A MALL PRETZEL WHEN YOU CAN HAVE *THAT?!*

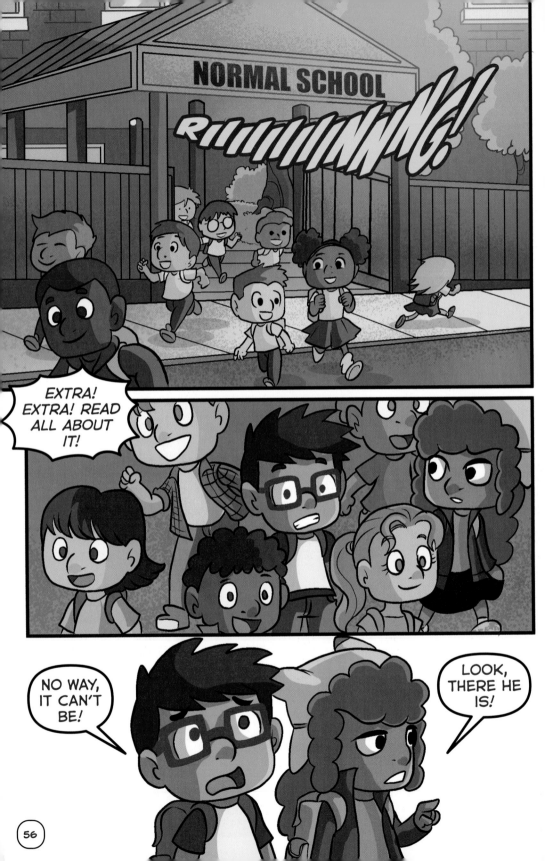

I SAY TODAY IS MONDAY, AND THE FLY ZONE IS CLOSED ON MONDAYS.

WHICH YOU WOULD KNOW...

...IF YOU FOLLOWED THEM ONLINE.

MEGABYTES! I WAS READY TO TAKE ON ANOTHER VID-WORLD.

AFTER DUSTING THOSE LEVEL-ONE CREEPS, THIS WOULD HAVE BEEN A BREEZE...

CHAPTER 5

THERE YOU ARE! YOU MISSED IT.

WE GOT THE *WIND RING!*

YOU CAN KEEP THE WIND RING.

I JUST WANT MY NOTEBOOK BACK.

WHAT IS SO SPECIAL ABOUT *THESE*?

THE TOWN OF NORMAL EXPERIENCED WHAT GROWN-UPS CALLED "AN ELECTRICAL DISTURBANCE" THAT NIGHT.

OH GREAT, NOW I'M GONNA HAVE NIGHTMARES.

THIS WASN'T JUST WI-FI GOING OUT.

PEOPLE WERE SEEING STRANGE STUFF ALL OVER.

EVERYONE LOST POWER FOR EXACTLY TWELVE MINUTES.

BUT ONE PLACE, SOMEHOW, *MAGICALLY* STAYED ONLINE WITHOUT A BLIP.

84

CHAPTER 6

HOP!

THUD

QUICK, SLIDE!

HOP!

JACKPOT! WE'RE SAVED.

NOW, POGO LIKE YOUR LIFE DEPENDS ON IT.

HAVEN'T WE HAD ENOUGH BOUNCING FOR ONE DAY?

WHAT? I MISSED DINNER.

CHOMP

CROSS THE STREET TO MR. HIGGINS'S YARD.

I HAVE AN IDEA!

UH-OH, I THINK I KNOW WHAT YOU'RE THINKING...

THUD

WAIT FOR IT...

WAIT FOR IT...

SNAP!

RAWWWRRR!

HISSS!

AFTER THE LONGEST MINUTE OF OUR LIVES, WE FINALLY *SAW THE LIGHT*...

THE POWER RETURNED TO NORMAL.

OH, THANK HEAVENS, THE WI-FI IS BACK ON!

WOO-HOO! WE'RE GONNA BE OKAY, KIDS!

103

EXTRA EXTRA EXTRA—

DID YOU HEAR THAT?

IT'S STARTING AGAIN!

EXTRA— XTRAAA...

GLITCH!

GLITCH!

WHAT'S WRONG WITH HIM?

HE'S GLITCHING BAD.

THE VID-WORLD IS TRYING TO CONTROL HIM, BUT SOMETHING'S OVERRIDING HIS PROGRAMMING.

THAT'S IT! THE WHOLE VID-WORLD IS GLITCHING. THINK ABOUT IT...

...WE GOT WATER MUTANTS AND SOME WATER-ZILLA THING.

WE DIDN'T GET WATER ZOMBIES...

DO YOU REMEMBER THOSE BEING IN *ZOMBIE INVADERS?*

WELL, NO, BUT I HAVEN'T FINISHED THE GAME.

TRUST ME: THOSE FREAKS-OF-THE-WEEK ARE *NOT* IN IT.

I DON'T THINK WE'RE PLAYING *ZOMBIE INVADERS* ANYMORE.

WELL, NOT THE SAME VERSION WE KNOW.

WHAT ARE YOU SAYING? THAT SOMETHING IS CHANGING THE GAME?

OR *SOMEONE.*

FOOOOM!

FOOOOM!

AND THAT'S HOW WE GOT TRAPPED IN A FIRE MAZE...

WE'RE GONNA BEAT *ZOMBIE INVADERS* ONCE AND FOR ALL.

BUT, WHATEVER YOU DO, *DON'T SNEEZE.*

UH-OH.

SNIFFLE! SNIFFLE!

YOU JUST HAD TO SAY THAT OUT LOUD!

NOW MY NOSE IS STARTING TO ITCH!

CHAPTER 9

SPLIIIIIIIISH!

WE GAVE THE FIRE ZOMBIES EVERYTHING WE HAD.

WE TRIED *WATER*...

HISSSSS!

...BUT THAT ONLY MADE THEM A LITTLE *STEAMED.*

AND I MEAN *LITTLE.*

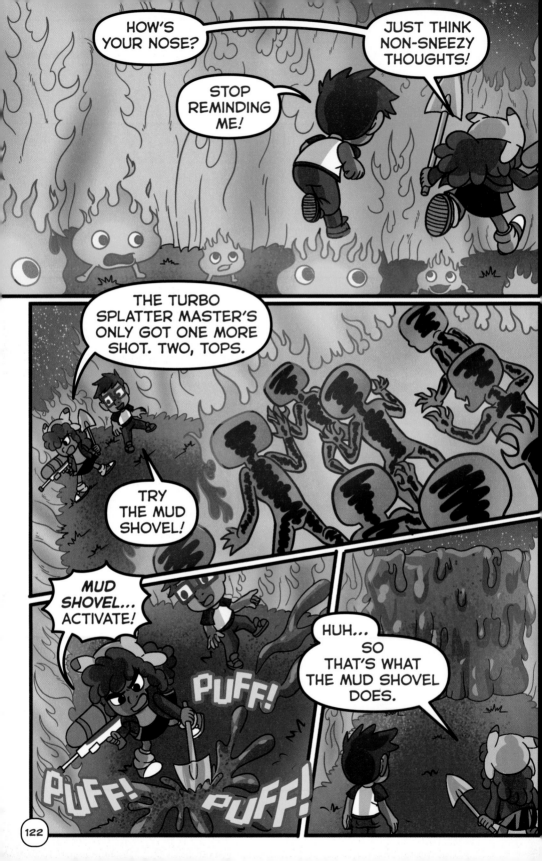

THE MUD SHOVEL SHOULD HAVE WORKED...

...BUT THIS VID-WORLD WAS PLAYING *DIRTY.*

THE FIRE ZOMBIES FOUND THEIR WAY TO US AGAIN!

I HOPE THIS WORKS!

WIND RING!

WOOOOOSH!

125

GLITCH!

...ALL OF THEM...

FOOOM!

WHAT DID HE SAY?

IT SOUNDED LIKE *"ALL OF THEM."* ALL OF THEM WHAT?

WELL, THAT'S NO HELP. WE'RE TRAPPED.

I SWEAR I'M CURSED AT THIS GAME.

THE CURSE!

SPLOSSSSH!

...COMBINING *ALL OF THEM*, JUST LIKE THE ZOMBIE PAPERBOY SAID...

...INTO ONE EPIC, AND TOTALLY DISGUSTING, ULTIMATE SPECIAL MOVE THAT WAS NOTHING TO SNEEZE AT.

WELL, IF THERE'S SUCH A THING AS A HIGH SCORE IN *ZOMBIE INVADERS*, WE JUST SHATTERED IT.

COULDN'T HAVE DONE IT WITHOUT YOU...

...AND YOUR ALLERGIES.

PLAYER ONE...

PLAYER TWO...

BLOW IT UP!

CHAPTER 10

YOU EVER SEEN GLITCHING LIKE THAT BEFORE?

WAS IT GLITCHING?

OR WAS THE GAME TRYING TO FIX WHAT *SOMEONE ELSE* HAD BROKEN INSIDE ITS CODE?

YOU REALLY THINK A *MYSTERY SOMEONE* IS CAUSING ALL THIS?

THINK ABOUT IT: IN VIDEO GAMES, THERE'S ALWAYS A BIG BOSS AT THE END.

AN EVIL VILLAIN WHO'S BEEN HIDING IN THE SHADOWS AND WAITING TO SURPRISE THE HERO ON THE LAST LEVEL.

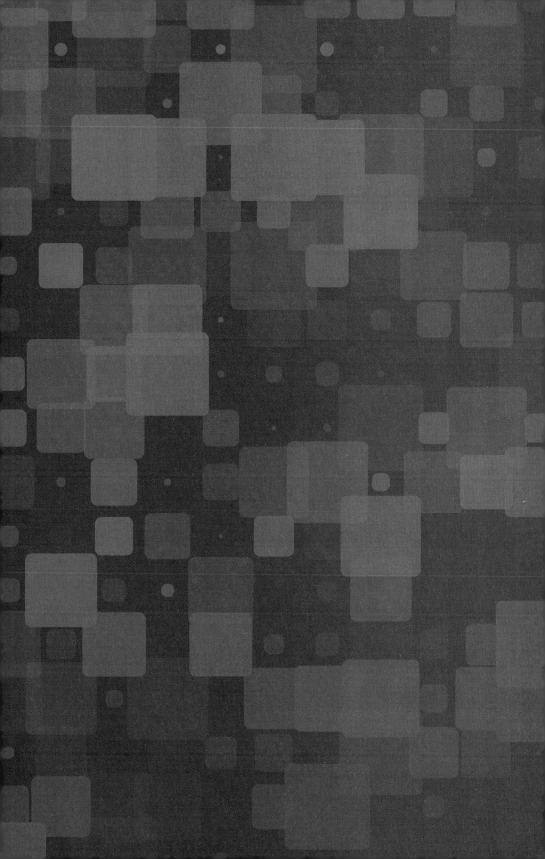

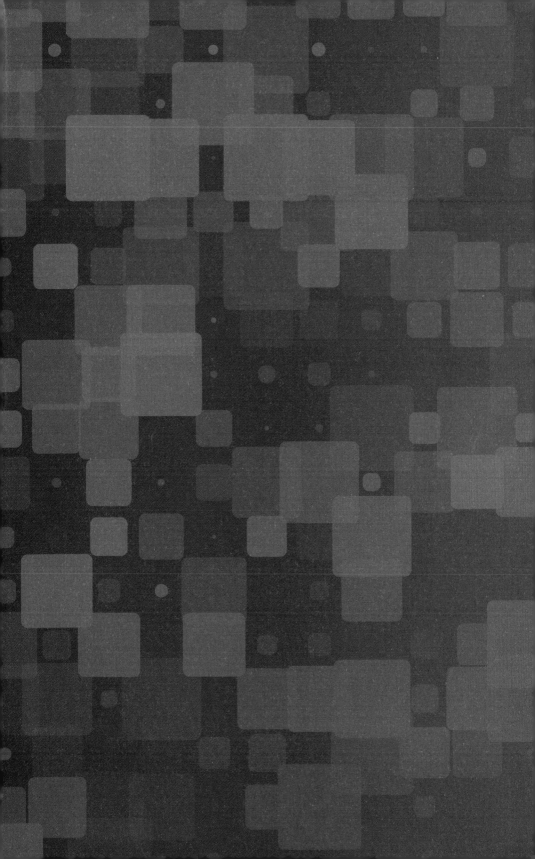

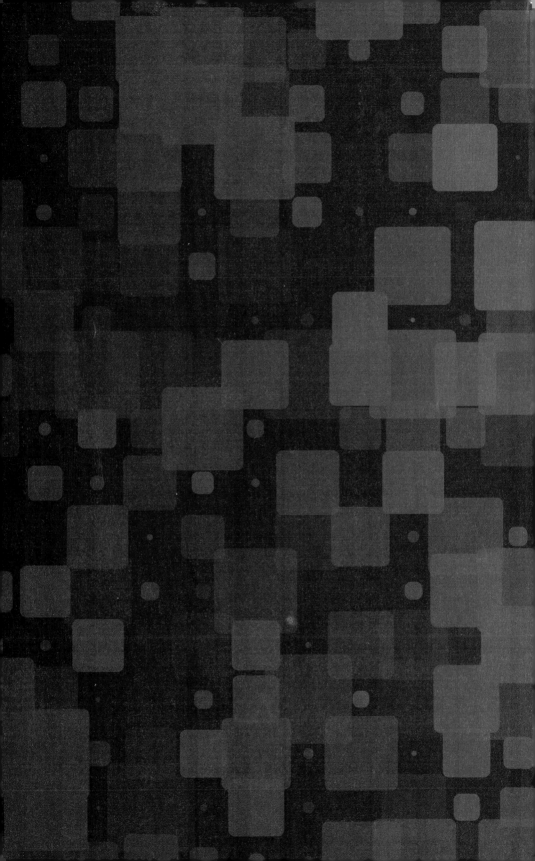